STRANGERS IN PARADISE

BY
TERRY MOORE

Under this picture, which ran on the inside front cover of the first issue of **Strangers In Paradise**, I admitted this was my first comic book and thanked a number of people who had helped me in one way or another. It was just last year but that seems so long ago now. Since that humble beginning I, like most all comic book creators, have become incredibly rich and powerful and now have factories all over the world cranking out Strangers In Paradise comics, lunchboxes, action figures and all the rest of the more than 4300 specialty items you've all grown to know and love. The SiP theme parks have expanded into 32 countries, rivaling even the BoneParks empire. I'm very popular in France.

All that from just three comics. Jeez, why didn't anybody tell me it was this *easy* ?!

...Heh heh, well I can dream, can't I? Truth is, I'm *still* in debt from last years big push to break into the comic book business and although SiP received critical acclaim, it had little bitty, microscopic print runs compared to the really big comics...like **Barbie**.

But that's okay, because all I really wanted to do was lose myself in this story about 2 girls and a guy who gets to know them. And I did.

I've never known a field to embrace the newcomers and help them along like the comics business. My continued thanks and gratitude go out to **Diana Schutz, Charles Phillips, Jeff Novotny, Tom Fassbender and James Eisele, Mark Herr, Carol and Sonny Denbow, Neil Gaiman, Bob Kahan, Wayne Markley, Jeff, Dave and Teri, Bill Stoddard** and my home buds at **Bedrock City Comics, Richard Evans** and **Bob Allen**.

The Collected Strangers in Paradise Volume No. 1, 3rd printing, August 1995 published by Abstract Studio, P.O. Box 271487, Houston, TX 77277-1487. All contents are © 1995 Terry Moore. Any similarities between any of the characters, names or establishments is purely coincidential and unintended. Nothing in this book may be reproduced without the express written consent of Terry Moore, except for purposes of review and promotion. This book contains some previously published material.
Printed in Canada

Contents

10 YEARS AGO... PUNCTURE HIGH SCHOOL.

MY LIFE IS SCRIBBLING AND SCRATCHING AND HALF FINISHED PAGES AT DAWN.

SENIOR PLAY ~~ STRANGERS IN PARADISE

IF ANYTHING, I'VE LEARNED YOU CAN'T ALWAYS GO HOME... YOU CAN'T ALWAYS BE WARM INSIDE. THAT *WITHOUT LOVE*, WE'RE NEVER MORE THAN **STRANGERS IN PARADISE!**

FRANCINE PETERS! YOU'RE ON IN TWO MINUTES!... LISTEN UP FOR YOUR CUE!

B-BUT MISS BEEM, THIS DUMB TOGA WON'T STAY UP!

DEAL WITH IT YOUNG LADY! YOU'RE NOT *COMPLETELY* STUPID, ARE YOU?

YEEUR NOT COMPLETELY STOOPID, ARE YEW?!

AAAGH!

YOU DON'T REALLY WANT ME TO ANSWER THAT, DO YOU?

KATCHOO!

KATCHOO! WHAT ARE YOU DOING HERE? I THOUGHT YOU WERE SUSPENDED YESTERDAY!

YEAH, WELL WHATEVER...

HEY! I COULDN'T MISS SEEING MY BEST FRIEND MAKE A FOOL OF HERSELF IN FRONT OF THE WHOLE SCHOOL, NOW COULD I?

OH GOD! HOW DO I LET MYSELF GET TALKED INTO THESE THINGS?

'CAUSE YOU'RE EASY GIRL! ...AND EVERYBODY KNOWS IT! YOU EVER HEARD OF THE WORD NO?

I AM NOT EASY! JUST BECAUSE I DON'T GO AROUND BLOWING UP GUYS' LOCKERS!

HEY! A GUY SCREWS ME AROUND HE'S GOING TO PAY FOR IT!

FRANCINE! WHERE IS THAT GIRL?

I BETTER GO.

OK... BREAK A BUTT!

LEG! I'M S'PPOSED TO BREAK A LEG!

GEE, SHOWBIZ IS HELL, HUH?

WHERE HAVE YOU BEEN? YOU'RE ON NEXT! GET OUT THERE!

...UH...I SAID, WHAT YOU NEED IS REFRESHMENT!........

BUT MY TOGA!

GO!

FADE TO BLACK...

RINNG!

BANG BANG

GOOD MORNING DEAR, SLEEP WELL? HEH! HEH! HEH!

KATCHOO!

GESUNDHEIT.

NO! I HEARD SOMETHING! LIKE SHOTS!...COMING FROM KATCHOO'S ROOM!

AAAGH!

PROBABLY JUST HER VIBRATOR BACKFIRING AGAIN!....I TELL YOU THAT GIRL NEEDS TO GET OUT MORE!

KATCHOO?! ARE YOU ALRI... GOOD GRIEF!

'MORNIN' FRANCIE. TOSS ME MY CIGARETTES, WILL YA? ≷ COUGH! COUGH! ≷

KATCHOO!?... WHAT ON EARTH HAVE YOU BEEN DOING IN HERE?

WHAT, NOW YOU EXPECT ME TO SAY SOMETHING PROFOUND? I WOKE UP, I SHOT THE CLOCK. HOW THE HELL DID YOU SLEEP?

LOOK, I'M SORRY IF FREDDIE AND I KEPT YOU UP LAST NIGHT. I TRY TO KEEP HIM QUIET, BUT YOU KNOW HOW IT IS.

WELL, SEEIN' AS HOW YOU TWO GO THROUGH THE SAME PATHETIC RITUAL EVERY NIGHT... I GUESS I KNOW EXACTLY HOW IT IS!

HAW MAN! WHAT'VE YOU BEEN DOING IN HERE KATCHOO... PLAYIN' WAR GAMES WITH YOUR BARBIES™?

WE'HELL! IF IT ISN'T REDDY-FREDDIE, THE WONDER DOG! HOW'D IT GO LAST NIGHT STUD, YA GET ANY?

SHUT UP!

OH THAT'S GOOD! "SHUT UP." I'LL CERTAINLY HAVE TO REMEMBER THAT ONE! ...HANG IN THERE REDDY MY BOY, EVERY DOG GETS A BONE, IF HE BEGS LONG ENOUGH!

IT WAS A JOKE FREDDIE.

YEAH WELL I'M NOT LAUGHING! IT'S HUMILIATING TO STAND THERE AND TAKE HER CRAP!... ESPECIALLY WHEN SHE'S *RIGHT!*

FREDDIE...PLEASE! LET'S DON'T GO INTO THIS AGAIN, I THOUGHT WE AGREED TO WAIT.

WAIT FOR WHAT FRANCINE? YOU NEVER SAY *WHAT* WE'RE WAITING FOR! ...GODOT? CHRISTMAS? THE EASTER BUNNY? ...*WHAT?!!*

LOOK, WE'VE BEEN ALL THRU THIS BEFORE! I THOUGHT WE HAD AN UNDERSTA...

I'M SORRY, TO ME THIS JUST DEFIES UNDERSTANDING.

I MEAN, HERE WE ARE IN A MATURE RELATIONSHIP, TWO CONSENTING ADULTS ...AND *YOU'RE NOT CONSENTING!*

HONEY, BELIEVE ME, IT'S NOT THAT I DON'T WANT TO...IT'S JUST THAT...WELL...

WELL *WHAT?!*

I...I... OH GOD, THIS IS SO HARD...

WHAT?!

I'M AFRAID IF I SLEEP WITH YOU...IT'LL RUIN EVERYTHING... AND YOU'LL LEAVE ME LIKE ALL THE OTHERS.

...YOU'RE JOKING RIGHT? I MEAN YOU CAN'T BE SERIOUS?!

NO! I MEAN IT! I KNOW HOW MEN ARE! YOU ALL HAVE THIS *CONQUEST* THING! THEN WHEN YOU GET WHAT YOU WANT IT'S 1-800 SEE-YA!

...FRANCIE? I'M SORRY. THIS IS ALL MY FAULT.... WHEN WILL I LEARN TO KEEP MY BIG MOUTH SHUT?

≷SOB≷

≷SNIFF≷ OH, IT'S NOT YOUR FAULT. THIS ISN'T THE FIRST TIME WE'VE FOUGHT ABOUT THIS.

WHY DO YOU PUT UP WITH THAT? IF I WERE YOU I'D TELL THAT GUY TO TAKE A HIKE!

I...I THINK I LOVE HIM.

WELL, I KNOW YOU DON'T WANT TO HEAR THIS AGAIN, BUT I'M TELLING YOU NO MAN IS EVER GOING TO LOVE YOU LIKE YOU WANT HIM TO... THEY DON'T KNOW HOW!

I DON'T BELIEVE THAT! I CAN'T BELIEVE IT! I...I JUST NEED TO BE MORE...TRUSTING, I GUESS. I MEAN, HE DOES HAVE NEEDS, I SUPPOSE... MAYBE.

LOOK FRANCINE, DON'T LET ANY MAN, ESPECIALLY THAT BUTT-HEAD, TELL YOU WHAT TO DO! YOU DO WHAT'S RIGHT FOR YOU... AND IF HE HAS A PROBLEM WITH THAT, TELL HIM TO GO JERK OFF!

...≷SIGH≷... I'M SO CONFUSED.

LISTEN, YOU DINGY BROAD, DO I HAVE TO SPELL IT OUT FOR YOU? THE GUY'S AN ASSHOLE, GOT IT?! HELL, THEY'RE ALL ASSHOLES BUT THIS ONE'S CERTIFIED!!

JEEZ, IF YOU JUST WANT SOMEBODY TO BEG FOR YOUR BODY EVERYNIGHT, I'LL DO IT! ... PLEASE FRANCINE?! PLEEESE?! OH FRANCINE! HOOOOOWL!

HAW?

BELIEVE ME, IF THAT FOOL HAD ANY HEART AT ALL, HE'D TELL YOU THAT YOU ARE THE MOST BEAUTIFUL, DESIRABLE WOMAN IN THE WORLD!

C'MON!

THAT EVERY NIGHT I DREAM YOU LOVE ME...

...BUT EVERY MORNING I'M ALONE.

...HUH?

OH FRANCIE...I LOOK AT YOU AND I SEE THE MEANING OF LIFE DANCING IN YOUR EYES.

KATCHOO STOP...

...AND I KNOW EVERYTHING WOULD BE OK IF I COULD JUST...

HEY! CUT IT OUT I SAID! I CAN'T DO THIS, UNDERSTAND?! I'M NOT... YOU'RE MY BEST FRIEND! WHY DO YOU KEEP...WHY DOES EVERYBODY KEEP TRYING TO...?!

JEEZ FRANCINE, IT WAS JUST A JOKE!...CAN'T YOU TAKE A JOKE?

SLAM!

STUPID! STUPID! STUPID! :SOB:

HELLO. THIS IS FRED FEMURS. I'M NOT IN RIGHT NOW, IF YOU'LL LEAVE YOUR NAME AND NUMBER, I'LL TRY AND RETURN YOUR CALL, BUT I AM A BUSY MAN! WAIT FOR THE BEEP!

MMM...FREDDIE? ARE YOU THERE?....WILL YOU PICK UP PLEASE?.........I MISSED YOU LAST NIGHT. ....I KNOW YOU DON'T BELIEVE ME, BUT I DID. ....YOU KNOW, IT WAS OUR ANNIVERSARY.............I WAS HOPING...UH... WELL, I THOUGHT LAST NIGHT WE'D BEEP! TOOOOOONE!

...SIGH

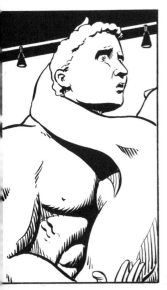

SCULPTURE

IMPRESSIONISTS

INTERESTING COMMENTARY YOU MADE ON THE RODIN BACK THERE.

SEXIST CRAP!

HMM... YOU SEEM INTRIGUED BY THIS PIECE THO'... WHAT DOES IT SAY TO YOU?

PISS OFF!

INTERESTING.

HEY! WAIT!

WAIT UP... PLEASE?!

WHAT ARE YOU, DEAF? WHAT PART OF *PISS OFF* DID YOU NOT UNDER-STAND?!

WELL, DO YOU MEAN THE SCULPTURE SAYS I SHOULD PISS OFF OR ARE *YOU* TELLING ME TO PISS OFF?

WHAT **DIFFERENCE** DOES IT MAKE? EITHER WAY YOU HAVE YOUR ASSIGNMENT... NOW *GET TO IT!*

IT MAKES A BIG DIFFERENCE TO *ME!*

EXHIBIT OF MAN
NOV 19   PM

I MEAN, DO I GIVE UP ALL HOPE OF EVER HAVING A CUP OF COFFEE WITH THE SCULPTURE... OR *YOU?*

MAIN ST. EXIT

DODG
BUILD

PSSST!...MARGIE...HI! IS FREDDIE IN?

AAH!

MISS PETERS! ...UH WELL YES...HE'S IN...

GOOD! I'LL JUST SNEAK BACK THERE.

BUT HE ASKED NOT TO BE DISTURBED.

MISS PETERS? MISS PETERS? PLEASE!

IT'S OKAY MARGIE...! I WANT TO SURPRISE HIM!

KNOCK! KNOCK! FREDDIE?

OH DEAR...

DAMMIT MARGIE! I TOLD YOU I DIDN'T WANT TO BE DISTURBED!

OKAY LOVER BOY! MERRY CHRISTMAS AND HAPPY EASTER! I'VE GOT A PRESENT FOR YOU!

SORRY! .... UH .... I WAS ... ... OMIGOD!

HEY, HEY, HEY! FRANCINE! HONEY! WHOA! ... UH, LISTEN BABY ... UH THIS ISN'T WHAT IT LOOKS LIKE!

HEY!

FRANCINE? FRANCINE!! WAIT! I CAN EXPLAIN!

≥ SOB ≥

MARGARET ... YOU'RE FIRED!

HMMPH!

A - T - C - O!

≥ SNIFF ≥

REFILL? IT'S DE-CAFF?

NO THANKS.

UH ... KATCHOO, YOU REALLY OUGHTA GET OUT OF THOSE WET CLOTHES OR YOU'LL CATCH COLD.

SPPLRT!

LOOK DAVID, EVEN THO' IT'S HIGHLY UNLIKELY WE'LL EVER SEE EACH OTHER AGAIN, IT'S IMPORTANT YOU GET ONE THING STRAIGHT!

NOBODY... ESPECIALLY A MAN IS EVER GOING TO TELL ME WHAT TO DO! YOU GOT THAT?!

OK...

SHUT UP! DON'T YOU DARE THINK THAT JUST BECAUSE I LET YOU BUY ME A CUP OF COFFEE, THAT NOW YOU CAN WORK YOUR WAY INTO MY LIFE AND SCREW IT UP!

I AM NOT SOME LONELY LOVESICK AIRHEAD, WAITING AROUND FOR MR. RIGHT TO COME AND SAVE ME FROM A LIFE OF SINGLE HELL!

BANG

I WILL NEVER EVER EVER BE YOUR BABY, YOUR MOTHER OR YOUR LOVE POCKET! AND IF YOU EVER LIE TO ME, I'LL FEED YOUR BALLS TO MY CAT!

PANT! PANT! PANT! PANT!

HOW ABOUT THAT DE-CAFF NOW, HONEY?

UH HUH.

THE NEXT MORNING...

≥ TICK TOK ≥
≥ TICK TOK ≥
≥ TICK TOK ≥

RING!!

FRANCIE?
...YOU AWAKE?

FREDDIE'S ON THE PHONE...DO YOU WANT TO TALK...

...TO HIM?

SWOOSH!

?

HELLO? FREDDIE? ARE YOU THERE?!

FRANCINE, LISTEN, WE NEED TO TALK...

WHY DON'T YOU MEET ME FOR LUNCH... SAY AT THE PARK, OK?...........
...WELL, LOOK, LET'S WAIT AND TALK ABOUT IT THEN, OK? SEE YA.

DON'T WORRY BABS, THIS WON'T TAKE LONG. THEN WE'LL GO EAT.

GOOD, I'M FAMISHED!

≡ SNIFF ≡

THIS SEAT TAKEN?

NOPE. ≡ SNIFF ≡

FRANCINE..... ABOUT WHAT HAPPENED IN MY OFFICE...

YOU DON'T HAVE TO APOLOGIZE FREDDIE, IT'S NOT YOUR FAULT!

...EH?

I ONLY HAVE MYSELF TO BLAME, I DROVE YOU TO HER.... I SEE THAT NOW. I JUST WANT TO WIPE THE SLATE CLEAN AND TRY TO **START OVER.**

WHAT? AND GO BACK TO THE WAY THINGS WERE? *NO THANKS!* I'VE HAD IT!

C'MON, YOU DON'T REALLY **MEAN THAT!** LOOK, I KNOW YOU LOVE ME AND I LOVE YOU... I'M READY TO TRUST YOU NOW, **REALLY!** I CAN MAKE YOU HAPPY!..... FREDDIE?

...I'M SORRY FRANCINE, I REALLY AM. YOU'RE A SWEET GIRL, BUT TO BE BLUNT... YOU'RE **NOT WORTH IT!**

FREDDIE, STOP IT! LISTEN HONEY, THIS IS *ME, FRANCINE!* I KNOW WHAT MAKES YOU HAPPY! **I KNOW** WHAT YOU WANT, WHAT YOU **NEED**...AND **I CAN DO IT!** YOU **KNOW** I CAN!

NAH! I DON'T THINK SO. LOOK, I HAVE TO GET GOING, I HAVE SOMEBODY WAITING IN THE PORSCHE.

I DON'T BELIEVE THIS! FOR CRYIN' OUT LOUD, DO I HAVE TO SPELL IT OUT FOR YOU? I'M TRYING TO TELL YOU I'LL SLEEP WITH YOU, OK?!

THAT **IS** WHAT THIS IS ALL ABOUT, RIGHT? I MEAN THAT **IS** WHAT YOU WANT FROM ME, ISN'T IT? WELL ALRIGHT... **I'LL DO IT**!

OH GIVE ME A BREAK! IT'S NOT LIKE I'M ASKING YOU TO DONATE A KIDNEY OR SOMETHING!

HELL! I DON'T NEED THIS CRAP! YOU WANT TO SLEEP WITH SOMEBODY? GO SLEEP WITH YOUR *LESBO GIRLFRIEND!* I NEED A REAL WOMAN!

HOW **DARE** YOU TALK ABOUT KATCHOO THAT WAY YOU SON OF A BITCH! I **KNEW** YOU'D DO THIS TO ME - ONLY YOU DIDN'T EVEN WAIT TO SLEEP WITH ME - YOU JUST DUMPED ME THE MINUTE I SAID YES! YOU **JERK**!

WELL, YOU'RE NOT WALKING AWAY **THAT** EASY BUSTER! YOU STARTED THIS, YOU'RE GONNA FINISH IT!

YOU EARNED IT FREDDIE, NOW **COME AND GET IT**!

UH, FRANCINE? ...WH-WHAT ARE YOU D-DOING?

GIVING YOU YOUR PRIZE! THIS **WAS** A CONTEST, RIGHT? SEE WHO CAN SCREW FRANCINE BEST!? WELL **YOU WIN** FREDDIE!

I'VE HAD IT! I GIVE UP! I CAN'T WIN! I'VE SPENT MY ENTIRE LIFE TRYING TO DO THE RIGHT THING...TRYING TO MAKE YOU OR SOME GUY JUST LIKE YOU HAPPY! AND YOU KNOW WHAT?... IT CAN'T BE DONE!

NOW WAIT JUST A MINUTE, I...

FRANCINE!

ZiiP!

HAVE YOU LOST YOUR MIND?! THIS IS A PUBLIC PARK!

THE PARK, YOUR OFFICE, WHAT DO YOU CARE? HEY, A MAN'S GOTTA DO WHAT A MAN'S GOTTA DO! RIGHT?

I CAN'T BELIEVE I LET THIS HAPPEN TO ME AGAIN! I LOVED YOU! I TRUSTED YOU! I WAS READY TO GIVE MY LIFE TO YOU!...AND ALL YOU WANTED WAS A PIECE OF MY ASS!

FRANCINE, JEEZ! BE REASONABLE! PUT YOUR CLOTHES ON BEFORE...

SWAP!

ALRIGHT...THAT'S ENOUGH! YOU'VE MADE YOUR POINT! NOW...

AAAAAGH!

THAT'S JUST THE POINT FREDDIE...

KA-PLAT!

THERE IS NO POINT!

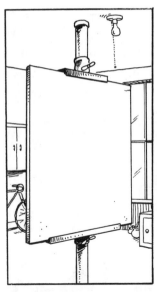

KNOCK
KNOCK

KNOCK
KNOCK
KNOCK
KNOCK

WHAT?

HELLO...KATCHOO? HOPE I'M NOT INTERRUPTING ANYTHING?

DAVID!

UH...NO. COME ON IN. I WAS JUST ABOUT TO QUIT ANYWAY.

SAY! ARE THESE YOUR DRAWINGS? ...MAY I TAKE A LOOK?

YEAH, SURE...KNOCK YOURSELF OUT.

LOOKS LIKE IT'S GOING TO RAIN AGAIN TONIGHT.

GOOD!

I LIKE THE RAIN NOW... IT REMINDS ME OF MEETING YOU.

OHMIGOSH, WHO'VE I LET IN MY HOUSE, PEPE LE PEW?

KATCHOO!...THIS IS AWESOME! I'VE NEVER SEEN ANYTHING LIKE IT!

SURE YOU HAVE! YOU TOOK GYM IN SCHOOL DIDN'T YOU?

NO, NO! I MEAN YOUR STYLE! IT'S SO STRONG! SO...SO BOLD!... SUCH A BIG VOICE FOR SUCH A DELICATE CREATURE.

YES?

DAVID?

...SHUT UP.

SKREEEEEECH

CRASH!

WHAT WAS THAT?

HOOOOUUUUUUNK!

FRANCINE!

PUT HER ON THE BED AND GET A BLANKET OVER HER! ...I'LL CALL A DOCTOR!

OKAY.

OH MAN!... SHE'S BEAUTIFUL!

I GOT A DOCTOR ON THE WAY.

YOU'RE KIDDING! HOW DID YOU GET A DOCTOR TO MAKE A HOUSECALL?

I KNOW HIS GIRLFRIEND.

SO?

HE'S MARRIED!

LOOK, GO CHECK ON THE CAR OR SOMETHING WILL 'YA? I DON'T WANT IT TO BLOW UP OUT THERE!

UH...OKAY,...GO KEEP THE CAR FROM BLOWING UP...RIGHT!

...OH FRANCIE! WHAT IN THE WORLD...?!

OH GOD! LOOK AT YOU! YOU'VE GOT GLASS ALL IN YOUR FOREHEAD! ...≤ SNIFF ≤ ...OH YOUR BEAUTIFUL COMPLEXION!

FRANCIE? WHAT HAPPENED HONEY? WHERE ARE YOUR CLOTHES? WHO DID THIS TO YOU?

...OH FREDDIE... DON'T....

FREDDIE?!!

FREDDIE!!

...YOU'RE A DEAD MAN!

To Be Continue

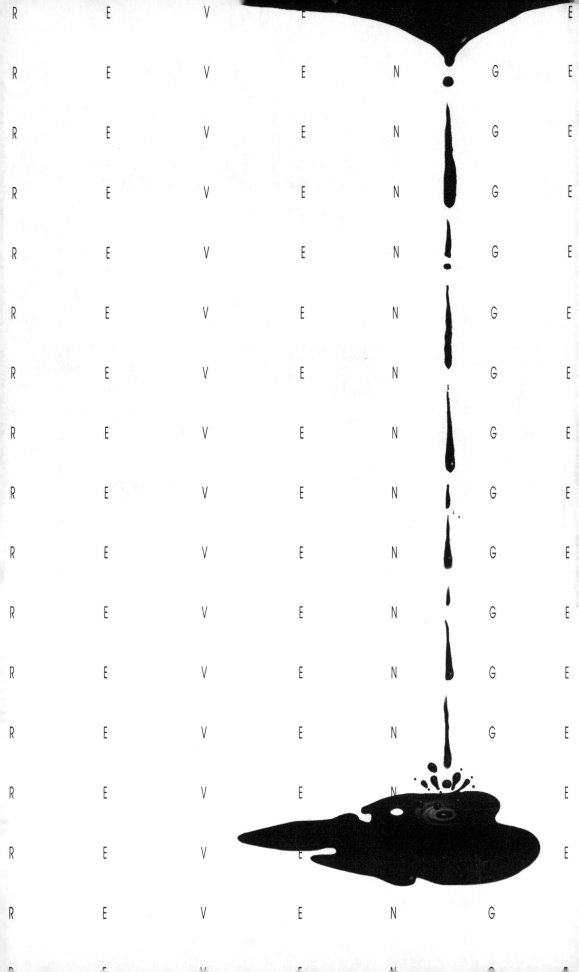

STRANGERS in PARADISE

LAST ISSUE: ALL *KINDS* OF STUFF HAPPENED! *GOOD GRIEF!* WHERE WERE *YOU*?! ACTUALLY, LAST ISSUE WE DISCOVERED THAT **FRANCINE** LOVES **FREDDIE** BUT HE JUST WANTS IN HER PANTS! AND IT WAS PRETTY OBVIOUS THAT **KATCHOO** LOVES FRANCINE BUT THAT **REALLY** FREAKS 'OL FRANCINE OUT! AND **DAVID** LIKES KATCHOO BUT SHE THREATENED TO FEED HIS BALLS TO HER **CAT!** THEN FREDDIE **DUMPED** FRANCINE WHICH MADE HER TOTALLY **FLIP** OUT, **RIP** HER CLOTHES OFF IN THE **PARK** AND RUN HER CAR INTO THE HOUSE! NOW FRANCINE LIES **UNCONSCIOUS** IN HER BED, KATCHOO IS *SERIOUSLY* PISSED AND FREDDIE IS ABOUT TO SUFFER THE **WRATH** OF...

KATCHOO'S REVENGE!!

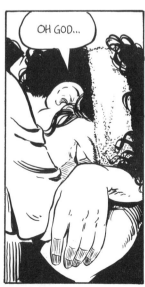

AND ONLY LEGENDS KNOW THAT ONCE THERE WERE GODS IN THE SEA...

GIANTS IN SIZE, WITH LULLABYE EYES, AND DREAMS...

...LIKE YOU AND ME.

BUT WHEN THE LANDS BROKE OUT IN WAR THE OCEANS IN BETWEEN...

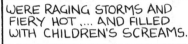

WERE RAGING STORMS AND FIERY HOT,... AND FILLED WITH CHILDREN'S SCREAMS.

A FEW SURVIVED TO SEE THE DAY, WHEN SUNLIGHT WAS DARK AMBER...

AND HEARD THE SOUND OF GODS AT SEA, LEAVING US... FOREVER.

..:SIGH:.. ...YOU'RE NOT GOING TO MAKE THIS EASY FOR ME, ARE YOU?

HOW DO YOU MEAN?

LOOK, I'M TIRED AND YOU'RE A MAN, SO LET'S DROP IT, OK?

I'M SORRY, I'M LOST HERE.

IT'S NOT GONNA HAPPEN PAL, YOU'RE BARKING UP THE WRONG TREE.

YOU DON'T KNOW ME, YOU BUY ME A CUP OF COFFEE...YOU READ POETRY...

I DON'T KNOW WHAT SOPHMORIC FANTASY YOU'RE CHASING HERE...BUT IF YOU THINK I'M INTERESTED YOU'RE SADLY MISTAKEN.

YOU WANT I SHOULD SPELL IT OUT FOR YOU? ...I'M... NOT...INTERESTED ...IN...MEN! OK?

'SCUSE ME... KATCHOO?

FRANCINE!

OH, WAIT... SO DIZZY...

YOU HAVE A MILD CONCUSSION HONEY, YOU NEED TO GET BACK IN BED!

WHAT HAPPENED?

YOU KNOW, I'VE BEEN DYING TO HEAR THE ANSWER TO THAT MYSELF.

I...I CAN'T RE-MEMBER ANYTHING.

YOU DON'T REMEMBER GOING TO THE PARK TO SEE FREDDIE?

FREDDIE?...WHO'S FREDDIE?

!

JUST TRY TO GET SOME REST, OKAY FRANCIE? EVERYTHING'S GOING TO BE ALRIGHT.

OH...MY HEAD...

KATCHOO?

IS SHE ALRIGHT?

NO, SHE'S NOT ALRIGHT! SHE HAS AMNESIA!

OH MAN!...WELL MAYBE IT'S JUST TEMPORARY. Y'KNOW FROM THE SHOCK AND ALL.

YEAH WELL, WHAT IF IT'S NOT?! WHAT IF SHE HAS BRAIN DAMAGE?!

OH MAN!

AND WOULD YOU STOP SAYING THAT! IT'S REALLY GETTING ON MY NERVES. YOU SOUND LIKE MAYNARD G. KREBBS!

WHAT ARE WE GOING TO DO?

WE?!

YOU STAY WITH FRANCINE, I'M GOING OUT!

SCREECH

WHOA! LOOK IT HER BURN RUBBER! HEH! WHY THE RUSH BLONDIE, HOT TO TROT? HEH!

RICHARD? WHAT ARE YOU DOING BACK THERE?

JUST OBSERVING VENUS, MY DEAR!

NOW... WHERE'S THE BRUNETTE? PROBABLY IN HER ≡HEH!≡ BEDROOM!

MMM... THAT'S NICE! GULP!

SAY! WHAT'S THE BIG IDEA...KICKIN' ME IN THE ASS!?

AW JEEZ. I'M SORRY.

I'VE JUST REALLY HAD A ROUGH DAY!

YOU SEE...MY GIRLFRIEND BROKE UP WITH ME TODAY.

I GUESS I'M JUST...HURT, Y'KNOW? I MEAN SHE WOULDN'T COMMIT, AND I WANTED ONE OF THOSE...UH, A UH, RELATED...?

A RELATIONSHIP?

YEAH, THAT!

OH YOU POOR GUY! YOU KNOW MOST WOMEN WOULD KILL TO FIND A SENSITIVE, CARING MAN LIKE YOU!

≷SIGH≷ I KNOW.

OH YOU POOR, SWEET MAN! SHE DOESN'T DESERVE YOU!

≷SNIFF!≷

MMPH! OH...THE PAIN!

WELL I KNOW JUST THE THING TO MAKE YOU FORGET ALL YOUR TROUBLES!

SLAM!

AALRIGHT! COUNT ME IN BABE! HEH! HEH!

HEY! HEY! HEY! CAREFUL WITH THE MERCHANDISE THERE! DON'T BE SO...

ROOOUGH!

COME ON EDDIE! I'M HOT TO TROT!

ALRIGHT ALRIGHT! KEEP YOUR PANTS ON!

NO WAIT... STRIKE THAT LAST COMMENT!

GIGGLE!

GINGER...WAIT...WAIT A SECOND...LET ME SHUT THE DOOR.

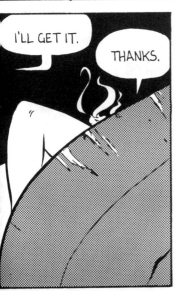

I'LL GET IT.

THANKS.

?

YOU JUST CAN'T KEEP IT IN YOUR PANTS, CAN YOU...READY FREDDIE?

CHOOVANSKI! WHAT DO YOU THINK YOU'RE DOING?! GET OUTTA HERE!

NAW, I DON'T THINK SO! OKAY SWEET CHEEKS, PARTY'S OVER. GET UP!

WHO ARE YOU... THE GIRLFRIEND?

GIRLFRIEND? HAH! THAT'S A LAUGH!

DON'T TELL ME YOU'RE MARRIED?! I ASKED YOU THAT BEFORE YOU BROUGHT ME HERE!

I'M NOT MARRIED ALRIGHT?!

THAT DOES IT!

DEBBIE! GET IN HERE!

'CAUSE I DON'T CARE IF SHE'S YOUR WIFE OR NOT, I STILL EXPECT TO BE PAID!

PAID?!! YOU'RE A HOOKER?!

TWEET!

GA-HAWD!

EEK!

DEBBIE...WHY DON'T YOU TAKE THE SWEET-TART FOR A WALK?

Girl Happy

HEY! PUT HER DOWN!

AAAGH! HELP! 911!

FREEZE! I WANNA TALK TO YOU!

EXCUSE ME? **PAY ATTENTION!** I SAID TAKE 'EM OFF!!

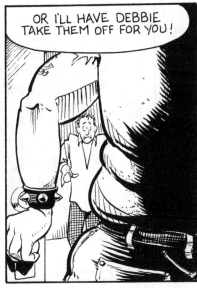

OR I'LL HAVE DEBBIE TAKE THEM OFF FOR YOU!

THIS IS **OUTRAGEOUS!** YOU'RE IN **A LOT** OF **TROUBLE** WOMAN! I HAVE FRIENDS IN *HIGH PLACES!* THEY CAN **FIX YOU**!!

OH REALLY? WELL MY BEST FRIEND'S LYING IN A **COMA**! YOU GOT SOMEBODY WHO CAN FIX **THAT**?!

SHE IS? FRANCINE? OHMIGOD.

DON'T PULL THAT ON ME! IF YOU'RE GOING TO **DESTROY** A WOMAN'S LIFE AT LEAST BE **MAN** ENOUGH TO **ADMIT** IT!!

I SWEAR I DON'T KNOW WHAT YOU'RE TALKING ABOUT! SHE WAS *FINE* WHEN I SAW HER... A LITTLE **UPSET** MAYBE...

SCRATCH

SHUT UP!

SLAP!

YOU MAKE ME **SICK!** YOU'RE *EVERYTHING* I **HATE** ABOUT MEN ALL WRAPPED UP IN ONE BIG BLOATED WART!

YOU DROVE FRANCINE **CRAZY!** YOU SCREWED HER UP WITH ALL YOUR **PRESSURE** AND **GUILT** TO SLEEP WITH YOU!!

I WANTED TO KICK YOU OUT RIGHT FROM THE START BUT **SHE** THOUGHT YOU **LOVED** HER! CAN YOU **BELIEVE THAT**?!

NOW THAT SWEET GIRL MAY BE PERMANENTLY **DAMAGED** BECAUSE OF YOU... YOU LOUSY SHIT!

I THINK THE **LEAST** I CAN DO IS MAKE SURE YOU NEVER DO IT **AGAIN!** ...TAKE OFF YOUR SHORTS!

NOW **WAIT** JUST A **MINUTE!** THIS HAS GONE **FAAAAR ENOUGH!** IF YOU THINK I'M GOING TO JUST STAND HERE AND LET YOU...

TAKE 'EM OFF I SAID! **NOW!!**

BANG

YOU'LL NEVER GET AWAY WITH THIS! **YOU HEAR ME?** I'LL GET YOU FOR THIS IF IT'S THE LAST THING I DO!!

WHAT'RE YOU GONNA DO?

HEH, HEH! GOT A PLUG?

AAAAAAGH!

SLAM!

HI... HOW'S SHE DOING?

GOOD... I THINK. VERY QUIET. SLEPT LIKE A BABY ALL NIGHT. YAWN

SPOKEN LIKE A MAN WHO'S NEVER HAD ONE.

SHE LOOKS BETTER. THE COLOR'S BACK IN HER CHEEKS.

YOU'RE A SWEET MAN TO SIT UP WITH MY FRIEND ALL NIGHT, DAVID. THANK YOU.

OH, THAT'S OKAY.

NO. I OWE YOU ONE.

YOU WENT TO SEE HER BOYFRIEND, DIDN'T YOU?

YEP.

I THOUGHT SO. I WAS WORRIED ABOUT YOU. WHAT IF HE HAD JUMPED YOU OR SOMETHING?

BELIEVE ME... HE WON'T BE JUMPING **ANYBODY** FOR A LONG TIME!

WHAT DO YOU MEAN?

MMM... LET'S JUST SAY I'VE DONE EVERY WOMAN IN TOWN A **BIG FAVOR**, OKAY?

FIZZT

...KATCHOO...UH... YOU DIDN'T...?

NO. BUT HE THOUGHT I DID... AND THAT'S ALMOST AS GOOD.

BESIDES, BY THE TIME THEY GET HIM DOWN, EVERY WOMAN IN TOWN WILL HAVE SEEN FREDDIE FEMURS FOR WHAT HE REALLY IS.

"GET HIM DOWN"?

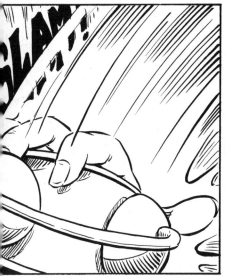

FRANCIE?
HOW YA FEELIN'...?

FRANCINE?

FRANCINE?!

FRANCINE!!

WHAT?

DING-DONG!

FRANCINE, I **SWEAR** I'LL GO TO THE STORE AND BUY SOME LIVER ... OKAY?

YOU PROMISE?

I PROMISE!

'CAUSE IT'S VERY IMPORTANT Y'KNOW.

I KNOW.

LIVER IS MY **LIFE!**

DON'T PUSH IT.

DING! DONG! DING! DONG! DING! DONG! DIN D

MY HEAD'S RINGING, KATCHOO.

THAT'S THE **DOOR BELL,** HONEY.

I'LL BE RIGHT BACK.

SHEESH!

BOY! WHO EVER IT IS THIS HAD **BETTER** BE GOOD OR...!

ALRIGHT! ALRIGHT! QUIT RINGING THAT FRIKKIN BELL BEFORE I CALL THE...

KA-CHIK!

...COPS.

ALRIGHT, TAKE HER DOWN-TOWN AND **BOOK HER**, BOYS!

AND LET'S NOT REPEAT HER LITTLE **JOKE**, OK?

WHAT'S GOING ON OUT HERE? KATCHOO?

FRANCINE! JEEZ, YOU LOOK **AWFUL**! WHAT HAPPENED TO YOUR HEAD?

WHERE ARE THEY TAKING KATCHOO?

TO JAIL! YOUR GIRLFRIEND TRIED TO **KILL ME** LAST NIGHT!

NO! I DON'T BELIEVE IT!

BELIEVE IT BABE! THAT WOMAN'S A **MENACE** TO **ALL** MANKIND!

AND **I'M** GOING TO SEE TO IT THEY PUT HER AWAY FOR A **LONG, LONG TIME!**

...FREDDIE!

FRANCINE...? ARE YOU OKAY?

...FRANCINE?

KATCHOO

KATCHOO?

KATCHOO?

KATCHOO?!

KATCHOO!

KATCHOO!!

FRANCINE ....WHERE'S KATCHOO?....DO YOU KNOW WHAT HAPPENED TO KATCHOO?

.......yes.

MARGIE, THANKS FOR HELPING ME WITH THIS.

LISTEN, IT'S MY PLEASURE. AFTER THE WAY HE'S TREATED ME AND YOU, HE HAS IT COMING!

I CAN'T BELIEVE HE FIRED YOU! I'M REALLY SORRY.

IT'S NOT YOUR FAULT. HE WAS JUST MAD BECAUSE I LET YOU CATCH HIM WITH ANOTHER WOMAN!

WHEN YOU CALLED AND TOLD ME HE PUT YOUR FRIEND IN JAIL, I STARTED THINKING...

WHAT DOES FREDDIE FEMURS HAVE GOING UNDER THE TABLE THAT HE WOULDN'T WANT ANYBODY TO KNOW ABOUT?

AND YOU THOUGHT OF SOMETHING?

OH! ARE YOU KIDDING?! THE GUY'S AS CROOKED AS THEY COME!

CLICK!

BUT THERE'S ONE ACCOUNT THAT REALLY TOPS THEM ALL... BERGER FOODS! HE'S BEEN OVERBIDDING THEIR JOBS AND POCKETING THE PROFITS FOR YEARS!

I KNOW HE KEEPS A SECRET RECORD OF HIS DEALINGS. IF I CAN JUST FIND...

...GOT IT!

SLAM!

SOMEBODY'S COMING!

HMM... I COULDA' SWORE I LOCKED THIS DOOR.

HELLO FREDDIE.

AAAGH!!!

SLAM!

FRANCINE! DAMNATION WOMAN! YOU ALMOST GAVE ME A HEART ATTACK!!!

HOW DID YOU GET IN HERE?

WELL...I...I, UH, I HAVE TO TALK TO YOU FREDDIE.

CLIK!

YOU DON'T HAVE A KITCHEN KNIFE ON YOU, DO YOU?

IF YOU CAME TO ASK ME TO DROP THE CHARGES AGAINST KATCHOO, FORGET IT!

NO...I DON'T CARE ABOUT KATCHOO ANYMORE, FREDDIE. ...I, I ONLY CARE ABOUT YOU!

YEAH RIGHT! WHAT ARE YOU DOING HERE FRANCINE? WHO...

CREAK

GULP

OH FREDDIE, PLEASE FORGIVE ME! I'M DESPERATE FOR YOU!!

WHAT DO YOU KNOW ABOUT BERGER FOODS?

ENOUGH TO SEND YOU TO PRISON.

YOU'RE BLUFFING!

NO... FREDDIE, I'M NOT.

I WANT KATCHOO RELEASED IMMEDIATELY!

UNDERSTAND?

YES.

I'M GLAD WE HAD THIS LITTLE CHAT. I FEEL SO MUCH BETTER, DON'T YOU?

I'M SORRY IT DIDN'T WORK OUT FOR US, FREDDIE, 'CAUSE I'LL TELL YOU A LITTLE SECRET...

I'M INCREDIBLE! BETTER THAN YOUR WILDEST DREAMS! ALL I WAS WAITING FOR WAS OUR ONE YEAR ANNIVERSARY!

WHICH WAS THE DAY YOU WALKED OUT ON ME.

GOODBYE FREDDIE.

SLAM!

FADE TO BLACK...

PENNY FOR YOUR THOUGHTS.

MMM... I WAS JUST THINKING HOW MUCH TIME I'VE WASTED WORRYING ABOUT OUR HIGH SCHOOL SENIOR PLAY.

STRANGERS IN PARADISE?

YEAH. YOU KNOW THE LINE WHERE THE GUY SAYS, "IF ANYTHING, I'VE LEARNED THAT WITHOUT LOVE, WE'RE NEVER MORE THAN STRANGERS IN PARADISE!"

AND THAT'S HOW I'VE FELT, GOING FROM ONE MAN TO ANOTHER, LOOKING FOR MR. RIGHT. AND WHEN I COULDN'T FIND HIM, I FELT LIKE I DIDN'T BELONG ANYWHERE.

BUT... I'M REALLY NOT A STRANGER AT ALL, AM I? I HAVE MY FAMILY... AND FRIENDS .... AND SOMEONE WHO LOVES ME VERY MUCH!

HOW COULD I HAVE BEEN SO BLIND NOT TO SEE THAT?

OH GOSH... ≷SNIFF≷ I'VE BEEN SO STUPID, HAVEN'T I?

YOU DON'T REALLY WANT ME TO ANSWER THAT, DO YOU?

HEH!

DINNER'S READY! LET'S EAT!

A TOAST! ...HERE'S TO *FREEDOM*... AND TO **FRIENDS** WHO'LL STAND BY YOU!

NO, NO. KEEP YOUR SEATS.

WISEGUYS.

GIGGLE!

AND TO MY BEST FRIEND ...FRANCINE,

...WHO IS, WITHOUT A DOUBT, THE MOST **DEARLY LOVED WOMAN** ON THIS GREAT BIG, **BEAUTIFUL PLANET!**

CHEERS!

WHAT...NO LIVER?

HA! JUST KIDDING!

OW!

THE END

JUST KIDDING, OF COURSE! ... I CAN WAIT TIL WE GET TO THE CAR!

...THAT WAS A JOKE, EINSTEIN!

OH GOSH, I'M SORRY KATCHOO, I GUESS I WAS DAYDREAMING. DID YOU SEE THAT GUY OVER BY THE HABERDASHERY?

≷ SIGH ≷ NO.

OVER **THERE**, THAT INCREDIBLE **HUNK** IN THE TWEED SPORTS COAT!

ZING!

I DON'T SEE ANY HUNKS IN TWEED COATS!

BUT HE'S **RIGHT THERE!** STANDING NEXT TO THE WOMAN WITH THE **BAD HENNA JOB** AND **TACKY TIGER STIRRUP PANTS!**

I SEE A SLIMY **WARD CLEAVER REJECT** AND THE **POSTER CHILD** FOR **PRO-CHOICE!**

≷ SIGH ≷ ...ISN'T HE WONDERFUL?

HE'S AN **ASS!** A COMPLETE AND TOTAL GRADE A ASS!

KATCHOO? .... UH, KATCHOO? DID YOU HEAR WHAT I SAID?

SQUEAL YOU PIG! SQUEAL!

KATCHOO?

HUH? OH! UH, SORRY. WHAT DID YOU SAY?

SALE

SHIR .5 OFF WOW

I WAS JUST ASKING IF YOU WERE READY FOR LUNCH... I'M HUNGRY.

OH. UH... SURE.

SO... WHERE DO YOU WANNA GO?

PIZZA?

I DON'T CARE.

OK.

SALE! SALE SALE

WAIT A MINUTE... I THOUGHT YOU SAID PIZZA WASN'T ON YOUR DIET.

I KNOW.

BUT THERE'S THIS REALLY CUTE GUY WORKING THERE NOW!

!

EXCEPT I THINK HE MIGHT BE ONLY 15! I CAN'T REALLY TELL. MAYBE IF YOU SEE HIM YOU COULD TELL, HUH? COME TO THINK OF IT, I HAVEN'T HEARD HIM TALK! ... HMMM... WHAT IF HE SOUNDS LIKE MICKEY MOUSE!

ALL BRAS FREE! WITH PURCHASE OF APPLIANCE

WARD... HOW ABOUT THIS ONE, DARLING? ... WARD? ... HONEY? ... WARD?! .... HEY BUTT-FACE!

sketchbook

WHERE DID YOU GET THE IDEA
FOR
STRANGERS IN PARADISE?

...is a question I've heard a a lot. "I dunno" I usually reply because the answer is so long and undoubtably boring I don't know where to begin. Truth is, I started out wanting to draw a newspaper comic strip and tried one idea after another before I realized I hated the gag-a-day life and really wanted to tell a story instead. Fortunately by that time I had quite an eclectic collection of characters and ideas to draw from. One of my earliest strips was about an enchanted forest filled with cigar smoking toads, wino owls, punk ducks and a beautiful blonde wood nymph named...

So Katchoo began as a happy-go-lucky wood nymph. Weird, huh? She did have a cousin named Madison though (sorry Teri!). Her manner may seem more familiar...

When guys talk to me about SiP, they always mention Katchoo. Even when she was a wood nymph, Katchoo always had the same effect on men...

For some reason, the syndicates didn't think my fantasy forest strip was wholesome enough. Hmm...I thought, wholesome. I resolved to create the ultimate wholesome comic strip, and what could be more wholesome than the all-American couple? I started a strip about the typical American domestic family of the 90's...loving, understanding, supportive, axe-weilding.

To my surprise, the syndicates didn't think that approach was appropriate for Americas newspapers either. Undaunted, I figured hmm...can't be the axe....it must be the toads. Lose the toads. And love, there's gotta be more love. Typical American love...

Needless to say, that strip is not running in over 2300 newspapers around the world today. Something about beds and inference. Hmph!

I was about ready to give it up when I tried one last idea. I had this Walter Mitty type guy, a chronic daydreamer, married to a patient and understanding wife named Francine. See, he's really out of touch with reality, see? And he lives in his own world most of the time...and if I have to explain it this much it must have been a really bad idea...but I did get Francine out of it.

If this strip didn't work though, I vowed to never do another comic strip again! Forget it! Blow it off! Burn the newspapers!...maybe I'd draw a comic book or something...